The Big Picture

A Systems Thinking Story for Managers

ISBN: 0-9677965-5-5
Published by Linkage Press
Copyright ©2001 Linkage, Inc.

LINKAGE *INCORPORATED*
One Forbes Road
Lexington, MA 02421
781.862.3157 tel
781.862.2355 fax
www.linkageinc.com

Linkage Press
One Forbes Road
Lexington, MA 02421
781-862-3157   FAX 781-860-5138
www.linkageinc.com

Printed in the United States of America.

ABOUT THE AUTHOR

Dr. Carol Ann Zulauf, Associate Professor in Adult and Organizational Learning at Suffolk University in Boston, co-designed the Master's Program in Adult and Organizational Learning, which focuses on applying systems thinking and organizational learning tools to practical applications. Carol is also President of Zulauf & Associates, a consulting company, which provides training in the areas of leadership and team development, systems thinking, and emotional intelligence. Carol is the 1995–1996 recipient of Suffolk University's "Outstanding Faculty" award; was nominated for the "Outstanding Faculty" award in 1999; and is the recipient of "Women Leaders" at Suffolk award, 1999.

About Linkage, Inc.

Linkage, Inc. is a global leader in creating organizational development, leadership, coaching and mentoring, and corporate education programs, research, and resources that achieve measurable business impact. Combining the world's most renowned thought leaders, "best-in-class" educational resources, and a highly experienced team of consultants, Linkage delivers programs to more than 12,000 individuals, including employees of 80 of the Fortune 100 companies each year. Clients include Lucent Technologies, Merck, Harvard University, Brigham & Women's Hospital, Skudder Kemper Investments, McDonald's, Toyota, Xerox, and a host of other organizations in all major industries.

EDITORIAL CREDITS
Louis Carter, Publisher/Consultant
Renee Bella & Jenifer Ng, Graphic Designers
www.linkageinc.com/

CONTENTS

SPECIAL ACKNOWLEDGEMENTS

A heartfelt thank you goes to Daniel H. Kim, Publisher of *The Systems Thinker*, for being an early collaborator with me on this project; to Laurie Johnson, Editor, Pegasus Communications, for her insights and feedback; Lou Carter, Publisher and Consultant at Linkage, Inc., and Jenifer Ng, Graphic Designer, Linkage, Inc., Renne Bella, Graphics Designer, Linkage, Inc., and Lynda Jemson, cover designer, Linkage, Inc. for all your help, guidance, and expertise.

With my Love
to My Wonderful Family
and Great Friends

"We are all the same."

—Diana Alexandrovna, a Belarussian woman who said this to me with a warm, embracing smile upon our first meeting in Minsk, Belarus, June 2000

1

Putting Out Those Fires!

This is the third day in a row it has rained. If there was one thing worse than a Monday, it was a rainy Monday. Allan was always feeling a bit overwhelmed by his workload, but today he felt even more harried than usual. There was a big customer demo (we really call it a dog-and-pony show back at the office) coming up and he was up to his eyeballs in trying to manage all the details. He had so much to do, it was hard for him to focus on where to even begin.

No sooner had Allan opened the door to his office, his telephone rang. It was Stewart, the VP of Sales and Marketing. It was never a good sign when Stu called. Calling first thing on a Monday was a doubly bad omen.

"Hi, Stewart. How's it going?" Allan tried to sound ten times more upbeat than he felt.

"Well, Allan, to tell you the truth, not so good. Rather than go into a lot of detail, let me just cut to the chase." He's always cutting to the chase, Allan thought to himself. What in the world does cutting to the chase mean anyhow?

"Go ahead, I'm listening," Allan heard himself mutter as he settled into his chair and put his briefcase down.

"Allan, you know how important this customer demo is to our company's success. We are counting on this demo to help us achieve our revenue targets. This customer demo is just two weeks away and, frankly, I am getting a little nervous about our readiness. You know that we are launching a brand new product that will help us leapfrog over our competition, but only if we are ready to show people real working units. Now, I know you and your team have been working very hard on this and you somehow seem to pull it off in the end. But, this time we have even more at stake than usual due to our disappointing results from last quarter. This demo has to really . . . blah . . . blah . . . blah . . .

As Stu went on and on, Allan began to wonder if Stewart knew what cutting to the chase really meant. If he did, he was definitely taking the scenic route.

" . . . and so if you need more help to keep things on schedule, I'll be glad to send some of my people over to make sure this demo will be the tremendous success we all know it needs to be." Coming from Stu, this sounded more like a threat than an offer to help.

"Well, thanks for the offer Stewart, but we have things pretty much under control here. I'll give you a full update by the end of the week." Allan hoped that would placate him long enough for him to find out what was really going on.

"Okay, Allan. I'll also check and see if Tom's available to join us for that update. How about two o'clock?"

"Great. See you then." Allan hung up the phone and muttered "great" again, except this time it was in the same tone you would use if you had just discovered you need a root canal. Tom was their president and good ol' Stu was making sure Allan knew how serious he thought the situation was.

He also knew Stu was right. Even though Stu was really forthright and extremely direct, he usually had great ideas and had a good pulse on what was going on. This customer demo is a big thing . . . a huge event for the company. Allan was starting to get nervous. In fact, he could feel a slight panic creeping up on him when he thought about the customer demo and the implications of having it be less than perfect. It has to be flawless! But the last thing he wanted to do was show Stu that he and his team were not capable of handling the challenge on their own. This was his job and his responsibility. Allan wasn't about to let a VP come in and take over his job. That would be tantamount to saying that he was incompetent.

And Allan was far from incompetent. He's been with this fast-growing high tech company for seven years now (an old-timer for this industry) and has been given increased responsibilities all along the way, having moved up from customer services rep, then to manager, and now to director of professional services. Allan is one of these hard-working, dedicated kind of guys. A lot of people respect him. He's always trying to do the right thing, although sometimes he tries-and pushes-a little too hard . . .

Allan was starting to get himself worked up into a frenzy. He knew he needed to talk to somebody fast, before he got himself even more worked up. As if on cue, Susan, the WOW (Whisking around On the Web) product launch team leader, popped her head in his doorway.

"Hi Allan!" Susan greeted him in her usual cheery voice. And not only was she cheery, she was also very perceptive. A very annoying combination for Allan at the moment. "Hey, Allan, you look like you've already had a rough week, and it's only Monday morning. What's up?" Sue is one of these people you can really rely on. She is very autonomous and only comes to see me when she's up against something that has her stumped and she needs a little coaching. She loves her new position of being team leader. She can really lead and bring out the best in others.

"I just got off the phone with Stu." He paused so Sue could register her own rendition of "great." Anyway, I need to talk with you about the customer demo. What's the status of the promo material?"

"Allan, we were supposed to have them back a week ago Wednesday, but Marketing keeps on delaying so they can do some last-minute stuff. I think Stu should work in his own backyard if he's worried about the product launch." Now, Susan was annoyed and perceptive.

Allan could feel the anger building up. "Why didn't anyone tell me about this delay?" What is Marketing doing with it for so long? What is it that they need?" Allan knew that he was starting to blow his top, but it was already too late to stop. The freight train had left the station and it wasn't stopping for any more passengers.

"Why can't you ever rely on them? Those brochures and packets should have already been put together by now. My God, they have to be shipped out by Friday!!" Allan started spewing out a barrage of questions that sounded more and more like accusations. Susan was starting to get that sinking feeling deep in her stomach. She hated it when Allan reacted this way. It always seemed to go this way, too. Blame, blame, blame . . . blah, blah, blah . . .

"I'm going to Marketing right now to find out what's delaying them!" Allan bellowed in the air.

Before Susan could respond or say another word, Allan was out the door.

Systems Thinking Principle: In physics, we learn that an action causes an equal and opposite reaction. In organizations, a reactive action causes an even more amplified reaction, usually in the same direction (Example:the blaming cycle)

Systems Thinking Causal Loop Diagram

A very quick glimpse of this "us" versus "them" blaming cycle can be illustrated as follows:
Figure 1: The "Us" vs "Them" Blaming Cycle

To read this diagram

As Pro Services' reactive, blaming behavior increases, Marketing & Sales will feel threatened. They will probably engage in reactive, defensive behavior, thus keeping this Reinforcing loop going.

Have you ever seen anything like this in your organization?

Learning Step #1

You need to stop and think—even for a moment—of how your words and actions will affect those around us.

2

Blamin' All the Way Around

"No, No, No, Allan, it's not us . . . it's Engineering." Bob said with absolute conviction in his voice. "We need the final written specifications from them so that we know we can create the comparison chart that shows why WOW is going to blow away all the current products in the marketplace. They've been keeping us waiting a little longer than we thought. I've sent them a dozen e-mails and left as many voicemails, but all I get from them is 'it's coming, it's coming.'

"Yesiree. If you want to know what the delay is, you should go see those guys. It's not us." Between Stu's 'cutting to the chase' and Bob's penchant for squeezing in a 'Yesiree,' wherever he could, Allan was getting more irritated by the minute. He turned around on his heels, muttered something under his breath, and headed towards Engineering.

His footsteps became more and more like stomping as he approached the archway that led into Engineering. He stopped by the secretary's cube to see if she knew what was going on, but she referred Allan to someone else. Allan stopped by the office of the Director of Engineering and hung out at the entrance, calling over to the Director.

"Hey, we need those final specs so we can get moving on this . . . you know the customer demo is only a couple of weeks away and we're slipping on our schedule . . . what gives?" Now, this is what you call cutting to the chase, Allan thought to himself.

"What's your problem this morning? Did you wake up on the wrong side of the bed this morning or are you always this friendly after the weekend?" Meg always had a good sense of humor which Allan usually enjoyed. But not this morning.

"I'm serious, Meg. Marketing tells me that they are held up because you guys haven't given them the specs they need to finish the promo materials."

"Oh, I'm not surprised that they would say that. They love to blame us for everything they are late on. The truth is, they can get the promo pieces 99% finished without our specs. When we do have them, all they have to do is drop the new spec numbers into the template and they're done. But listen, I don't have the numbers to give them because I haven't gotten the test results back from manufacturing. If you want the stuff sooner, go talk to those guys."

Allan had just about had it as this point. He stormed out of Engineering and headed for Manufacturing's Prototype and Test labs.

He tried very hard to restrain himself as he went through the whole story with the Assembly and Test manager. George nodded sympathetically as he listened to Allan's story.

"I agree with you, Allan. We need to get the prototype tested and the results out the door. But we haven't been able to run the tests because we are waiting on our supplier to send us the front LCD display panels. Besides, all my guys are flat out running tests and trying to debug problems with our current products."

"I can't believe this! Doesn't anybody else care about the success of this customer demo but me? It's the future of the company we're talking about here! I've had enough of this run around. You know if you want a job done, you have to do it yourself." With that, Allan turned and walked out before George could even open his mouth to register a protest.

Systems Thinking Principle: Chasing things at the event level only leads to more events, not deeper insights. A blaming mission accomplishes its mission and nothing else. Plus, it's stressful!

Figure 2: The Blaming Mission

Learning Step #2

Rather than just reacting to a particular event, see how many times this "event" has occurred before . . . in other words, look for a *pattern*. Then, before all the blaming goes around in an organization, ask "What am I responsible for?"

3

Personal and Organizational Issues Collide

It's Friday afternoon, and Allan is feeling pretty good. Yup, he thinks to himself, if you want something done right, do it yourself. He knew he was feeling self-righteous, but at the moment, he was feeling too proud of himself to stop. Of course, he had to do without a whole lot of sleep and he didn't see his family very much the rest of that week, but things were back on track with the customer demo. He had even managed to get the promo piece finished in time for the meeting with Tom and Stu. Seeing the surprised look on Stu's face in itself was worth all the long hours. Nobody could say that Allan wasn't reliable! He was as dependable as a rock, he thought to himself as he puffed up his chest.

Allan was feeling so good about taking back control of the customer demo project that he could hardly wait to tell his wife as soon as he got home. As he entered through the front door, he could hear someone chopping up something in the kitchen with such a vengeance, it sounded like an ax splitting logs or a scene from a grisly horror movie. He walked into the kitchen to find his wife hammering away at a poor stalk of celery with a meat cleaver, or what was left of it.

"Whoa! I would hate to be whoever or whatever that celery is reminding you of right now." Allan tried to tease her as he put his arms around her from behind and gave her a hug. She responded with a half-hearted hello and continued to mince the celery into ever smaller pieces. Whoever said that it is men who crawl into their caves when things are going badly? Allan mused. My wife can go from being so cheerful one moment to being really ticked off the next if something really pushes her buttons.

"Okay, Vicki, either we are out of potatoes and you are making us mashed celery instead, or something didn't go well at work." Actually, Allan hoped that she really was making mashed celery because that would certainly be a lot simpler than the other alternative, but he had a sneaking suspicion it was about work. Vicki didn't even like celery.

"YOU WON'T BELIEVE WHAT HAPPENED TO ME TODAY!!! I AM SO ANGRY!"

"Maybe you can take a deep breath and tell Dr. Allan all about it." He had wanted to tell her his good news about getting the customer demo project on track, but this didn't seem like the right time for him to be gloating over his accomplishments. Allan wasn't the most sensitive type of guy, but this wasn't hard for even Allan to miss. Clearly, she is distressed.

"I had to get this report out by 3 o'clock so we could courier it over to our clients. Well, things were a little tight, but I knew what I needed to do to finish it by that time so I stepped out for lunch. As I am returning, I hear typing coming from my cubicle, and what do I find? MY BOSS IS FINISHING THE REPORT ON MY COMPUTER!! I was stunned, embarrassed, furious! It was a clear sign that he didn't trust me! He didn't think I could do it so he just stepped in and did it himself!" As she was describing the scene, Vicki pointed her finger straight at Allan when she referred to her boss. Allan was getting another sinking feeling in his stomach. It was feeling like Monday all over again.

"Now, wait a minute, Honey," Allan said in his best consoling voice. "There is nothing wrong with what he did. I'm sure he was just trying to help."

"NOTHING WRONG? Trying to help? How can you say that?" Vicki asked incredulously. "Allan, he might as well have told me right to my face that he didn't think I could do it! How would you like it if your boss told you he didn't have confidence in your abilities?"

Allan found himself nodding in agreement almost unconsciously as he recalled how he felt after Stu's phone call. But then he winced at the thought of what his behavior must have seemed like to his project team. He found himself trying to defend her boss's actions (as well as his own). "Maybe he was just focused on making sure the client got what they needed, that's all. Maybe it wasn't meant to convey anything about your competence."

"No. I felt like he didn't trust me. Allan, how would you feel if your VP gave you a job and when he thought it wasn't going to be done on time, just took over? How would you feel about that?"

Allan gazed down at the floor. He knew his wife was right. It didn't feel too good. Allan was squirming on the inside. This sounded too close to what he had done to his team. But, no, he protested to himself . . . this is different . . . he hadn't actually gone into their cubicles. Besides, with the customer demo less than two weeks away, he had to do something. Everybody was just waiting for someone else. He had no choice but to act and act fast. If he hadn't gone to meet with the supplier face to face and pushed that part through the system, who knows where they would be.

Allan had another worrisome thought. If his wife was this upset about her boss, could his people be complaining to their significant others about what he did? Was there really something for them to gripe about? This thought gnawed at him all weekend.

Systems Thinking Principle: Being aware of what's going on is the beginning of a cure.

Learning Step #3

How aware are you of your own actions on others? Spend just a few minutes each day reflecting on how your words, actions, behaviors affect others.

4

Team Becomes Dysfunctional

Allan was simultaneously relieved and anxious as he drove into work on Monday. He was relieved that the weekend of waiting and wondering was over. But, he was also anxious about what he would find with his team. He had been so focused on getting a lot of tasks done, he hadn't really noticed where people were.

When he walked through the office, the usually cheery Susan barely looked up at Allan as he said hello. He flipped on his computer and scanned the few e-mails from his team giving him updates. As the day wore on, he got the feeling that people were avoiding him. When he reflected over the previous week, he realized that there hadn't been as many face-to-face chats, and that people had been leaving voice mails instead. He had attributed that to the frenziness of the week before, but now he wasn't so sure that was it. He had a strange feeling that he was somehow being systematically isolated. "Cripes," he muttered to himself, "I must be getting paranoid in my old age."

Walking down the hall, he noticed how quiet it was. As he walked by the glassed-in conference room, he spotted his whole team deep in discussion-without him being there. He thought about walking in to ask what was up, but he had a strange feeling that if he did that, their answer would just be silence. He decided to go back to his office.

He quietly shut the door and slumped down at his desk, staring at the screen saver on his PC. He was feeling angry, confused, and sad all at the same time. Well, at least now he had real reasons to be paranoid about, but that was hardly a comforting thought.

As the week wore on, he felt the isolation on two fronts: interpersonal and informational. His people were just leaving messages and sending e-mails instead of stopping by his office. It was almost as if they were avoiding him. The other isolation was being cut out of the information loop. People gave him whatever information he asked for and not a single byte more.

He gazed out the window. The customer demo was now only two days away and although there was still a lot of work left to do, it was now a matter of routine tasks. So why weren't people happy that they were well prepared for the customer demo being a success? For that matter, why wasn't he feeling happy that it was going to be a success?

Feeling like he could use some cheery company, he called his wife and asked her if she were free to meet him at their favorite Italian restaurant for lunch. Thankfully, she was.

They were seated at a quiet table near the window. After talking about the kids and how they were doing in school this semester, Allan steered the conversation towards how things were going with her boss, especially after "the incident."

"Well," Vicki began, "I decided to hang back and just keep it cool."

"What do you mean by 'cool'"?

"Well, I just keep to myself for the most part. I still feel very embarrassed, I really feel like I failed; that I was incompetent. I don't want to look him in the eye, so I avoid him and just do my work." She fell silent for a moment.

This was all hitting too close to home for Allan. He found himself trying to come to her boss's defense again. "Vicki, what if your manager had no intention of his action reflecting badly on you. What if all he wanted to do was pitch in and make sure the client got what they needed?"

"I don't have a problem with him wanting-needing-the job done by that time. I knew it had to be done by then. If he had doubts or concerns, he should have talked to me about it. If he was doing it to help, he should have offered me help. Why did he have to finish it for me?"

"Well, that's a good question. Why don't you ask him and find out what he was thinking?" Allan almost wanted her to ask him the question so he could give her the explanation that he wanted to give to his own staff.

"I don't know, Allan. Sure, I can sit here and talk about these kinds of things with you, but it's not that way at work. I don't feel like I can be as open with my boss."

She had a point. Allan didn't talk about his feelings with his boss, either. Nor with his staff for that matter. "Well, all I know, Vicki, is that, from a manager's point of view, there is a lot that has be to managed, and looked after, and followed-up on. The demands are endless, day in and day out. We barely have the time to strategize about our future direction, everyone gets so caught up in putting out those ever-present fires. There is just so much to do . . . I have so many challenges to face that maybe in my haste, I might hurt somebody's feelings, but I don't mean to. That doesn't make be a bad boss."

"Allan, are we talking about my boss or are we talking about you?"

"Uh, well, I was just putting myself in your boss's place." Allan tried to recover from his slipup, but his wife looked at him with a suspicious smile.

> **Systems Thinking Principle: Although the intended consequences of your actions may or may not happen, the unintended consequences always happen.**

Learning Step #4

What can help in solving a problem is to (a) tell it like a story (b) ask 'what is influencing what' in this story and (c) identify the consequences of possible actions before those actions are implemented.

5

Dynamic Repeats in Michigan

The customer demo turned out to be a huge success. WOW got rave reviews from the press and they collected advanced orders that exceeded their most optimistic projections. The only trouble now was trying to actually fill all the demand they had generated. At the moment, that was a good problem to have.

As Allan was savoring the moment, his thoughts were interrupted by a phone call from Stu. It was one of those "congratulations, and here's what else you can do for me" kind of call. Yes, he did a great job, and he knew all along that Allan could do it, but now there was a problem with an upcoming event in their Michigan office.

"Allan, we need someone of your caliber to go to our office in Michigan to help out with their customer demo that is coming up next Friday; the guys seem to be stuck. We need for you to do there whatever it was you did for this successful demo."

Allan knew he was being buttered up, but at this point he was feeling a little starved for some stroking so he just soaked it all up. At least he felt affirmed in his actions. He headed home to pack and called his travel agent from his car to book a flight for that evening.

The next day, Allan made his way to the engineers at the Michigan site to find out what was going on. Just then, Jack, their team leader stormed in and started to tear the demo room apart, taking down equipment, moving tables, wheeling around the VCR, all the while grumbling that nobody knew how to make this look as good as he did. He started to bark out orders; people started scurrying. It looked like a chaotic mess. The engineers turned to Allan and confided, "You know, he's really not such a bad guy when he isn't under all this pressure. He just turns into a controlling maniac whenever the pressure is on."

Allan didn't exactly need things spelled out for him. What he saw in Jack was a mirror, and he didn't like what he saw reflected back.

Systems Thinking Principle: A mirror allows us to see things our unaided eyes are not able to see. The eye cannot see itself.

Learning Step #5

Call in a trusted colleague, consultant, friend to talk with about your perceptions, questions, insights, and courses of actions that you are contemplating. We all need that input from others and it is a sign of strength, not weakness, when we can seek input and guidance from others.

6

Insights Are Where We Least Expect Them

Allan was completely engrossed in his thoughts as he slumped into his seat on the plane for the flight back home. There was something that just clicked within him when he saw Jack running around. There were just too many similarities between how he interacted with his staff and what he observed Jack doing. And to think, they're both good guys, too! It was then that he noticed his seat mate sitting next to him, a white haired elderly gentleman in his early sixties. No, actually he looked much younger physically, but there was something about his eyes that made him appear much older. He couldn't quite place it, though.

"You seem perplexed about something," the stranger spoke.

"Well, I am," Allan answered back unhesitatingly. "But I really don't know how to explain it exactly.

It's just this nagging thought I have, but it isn't clear to me what it means or what I can do about it."

"I've found that talking things out helps me to see things that I hadn't seen before. It's as if the talking process itself can make things clearer. I'll be happy to listen, if you want to talk about it." It was such a genuine and simple offer, Allan could hardly refuse.

"You're on!" Allan said enthusiastically. Then he began to tell the older man what had happened from the time that he got the call from Stu to his conversation with his wife about her situation to this visit to their Michigan office.

"So anyway, to make a long story short, I got the job done and the customer demo was a huge success. But, as time goes on, I am feeling less and less good about what I did. I have a nagging feeling that I'm missing something."

The stranger sat quietly for a minute, as if he were allowing Allan's words to slowly soak in. He then asked if Allan would mind if he were to ask some questions.

"Shoot," Allan invited.

The stranger wrote the word "Events" at the bottom of the napkin and asked Allan to tell him what he had noticed that led him to take the actions that he took.

"Well, I saw that people weren't doing their jobs. They were just . . ."

"Excuse me," the man stopped him in mid-sentence. "I'm sorry to interrupt, but please allow me to clarify what I was asking for. I wanted to know what specific conditions you saw or what events you saw happening that led you to take action. In other words, what led you do draw the conclusion that people weren't doing their jobs?"

"Oh, I see. You're saying that "people not doing their jobs" is not really an event. The man nodded.

"Well, I guess the event that precipitated all of this is when our VP of Sales and Marketing called me and asked about how the customer demo preparations were coming along. Even though I told him that things were fine, it heightened my concerns about the progress we were making. So, I started to ask around because I just knew that things weren't moving fast enough."

"How did you go about asking around?" the man asked with an eyebrow raised.

"I asked Susan, the team leader in charge of this project, what the status was and she gives me a lame answer about marketing holding things up. I guess I got a little upset with her." Allan found himself squirming as he heard himself recount the situation.

The man was listening so intently to Allan it was almost unnerving. He wanted to know what happened next. Allan told him about the long string of people passing the buck until he got so fed up with it all that he decided to take over and just do it himself. The man stopped him at that point and asked Allan if he could recall what exactly went through his mind when he made that decision.

Allan thought for a minute and gave a tentative response. "I think I said to myself something like 'People are always letting me down. If I want a job done right, I have to do it myself.' It was something like that."

And what thoughts was he thinking about all those people, the man wanted to know. This line of questioning was making Allan a bit uncomfortable. He wasn't used to thinking about his thinking; he was more used to acting on his thinking. It felt like an unnatural act.

"I have to admit that I felt they were incompetent and could not be trusted to complete the job on their own. I know that sounds kind of harsh, but I'm not just basing it on this one project." Allan found a need to defend himself as he revealed his thinking to this stranger sitting next to him. "This very same thing happened on at least two other projects. In both cases, I had to step in and bail them out to save the project . . . and their butts!"

The stranger seemed almost pleased to hear that this had happened before, but Allan wasn't sure why he might be glad about that. As Allan was pondering on what to say next, the man asked him another one of his "thinking" questions.

"Why do you think this same thing is happening over and over?"

Allan wasn't quite sure what to make of this question. He thought he had already answered this by telling him that the people were incompetent, even though he hated saying it that way.

"If they are all so incompetent, why don't you fire them and hire more competent ones? Or if you can't fire them, at least get them reassigned so that you can get people who are more competent?"

This was really making Allan squirm. He felt his face flushing red. He hadn't meant to imply that his people were totally incompetent. It just seemed to happen in particular situations like this one with the customer demo. He tried to straighten things out because even though this was a stranger, he didn't want the man to walk away thinking something that wasn't true.

In response to Allan's explanation, the man began to ask Allan a series of questions.

"So, what I hear you saying now is that most of the time your people are highly competent in doing their jobs?"

Allan nodded.

"But there are specific situations where they seem to be consistently incompetent?"

Again, Allan nodded.

"And the one thing common about each of those situations is that you are directly involved in all of them?"

Allan stopped in mid-nod. "Hey, wait a minute. Are you saying what I think you are saying?"

"I am only playing back to you what you have told me," the man replied with genuine innocence. "Am I not being accurate in some way?"

"I guess you are. It's just that when you put it that way, it sounds like I'm the one causing the problem when in fact, I'm the one solving the problem!" Even as he said this, Allan found himself less than convinced of his own statement. Was he just pointing the finger of blame on everyone else, just like he had accused everyone else of doing? Was he really the solution or was he part of the problem?

All this thinking and reflecting was making him feel very uneasy. No wonder I don't do this reflection stuff often, Allan thought to himself—it's hazardous to one's sense of self-righteousness!

"Gee, are you saying that I am the problem?" Allan asked.

"I'm not drawing any conclusions at this point. I'm just curious about exploring what other possible explanations might be causing the behaviors you have been describing. There is one thing I would caution you on, if you are interested in hearing it."

Allan paused for a minute. He wasn't sure he was ready to handle receiving advice from this person who had already given him some zingers to think about. Nonetheless, he did appreciate his offering instead of just giving his advice. Allan made a mental note to himself about trying to do that more often himself.

"Yes, I think I am ready to hear it."

The man chuckled. "I'm sorry. I seem to have you all worried about what I am going to say. I don't mean to make you feel uncomfortable, although I have to admit, most people seem uncomfortable with the kinds of questions I ask. Anyway, my word of caution is to notice when you find yourself engaged in dualistic thinking."

Allan wanted to know what he meant by dualistic thinking.

"It's a very common trap that most managers can get stuck in. It manifests itself in either-or thinking of this or that and in polarized views of right or wrong. What I heard you do was go from saying that your workers were causing all the problems to wondering if you were the cause of all the problems. Reality is usually somewhere in the middle of any polar extremes. It may be more beneficial to begin by asking 'what' is causing our problems than 'who'."

"Whew! I feel better already about this kind of approach." Allan was genuinely relieved. If there was one thing he hated to do more than blaming others was blaming himself. This seemed like a much better way to view things.

Systems Thinking Principle: Blaming others doesn't solve the problem. Sometimes we need to stop to ask how we are contributing to the problem, too. This will aid in our own emotional development.

Learning Step #6

This is a big leap forward. Ask yourself how you may be contributing to the problem. All of us—at one point in our lives or another—have cast the blame outward, onto others, without asking if we had some part in the situation at hand.

7

Seeing Patterns

Allan could hardly wait to get to his car so he could think more about what the man on the plane had to say. He seemed to have insights of how things worked. He viewed things from a different perspective. Rather than just reacting to events which is so pervasive in his organization (Heck, Allan mused to himself, "Every organization!") and, it seems, so counterproductive in the long run, he seemed to ask broader questions to get to the underlying causes. Hmmm, Allan continued to think. And those questions focused on trying to figure out how many times something has happened to see if it really is a "problem" rather than just placing blame on a person. A slightly pensive crease crossed Allan's brow as he contemplated the next thought . . . we even get to see if we are part of the problem instead of pointing that finger outwards.

Allan started to think about the customer demo. It was such a success, and yet his people felt rebuffed, like they really weren't a part of all the glory. But, it goes like that, he continued to ponder. We go along until just a couple of weeks before a customer demo and then really dig in . . . what's wrong with that? And, for this demo, goodness, look at the orders that came in!! Sure people are really busy now ramping up to fill all of those orders for our WOW product and we have a lot of reworks . . . his mind wandered.

As Allan pulled into the driveway, still engrossed with this customer demo dilemma, he pulled a piece of paper from his briefcase and sketched how he saw what was going on. Allan chuckled to himself. His wife Vicki would always chide him for "analyzing things."

So, we go along, things are pretty steady and then we really go gangbusters . . . putting in a lot of OT. Did this for Model I, for our customer demo last Fall. Did it this time. Actually, Allan continued to think, usually 60–70% of our time spent on the product launch for the customer demo happens in the previous 2–3 weeks before the actual demo!! Allan even labeled his graph. He called it "The Customer Demo Cycle." He looked at it for a few minutes.

This frantic pace right before the major event caused everyone to run around like crazy nuts—

Figure 3

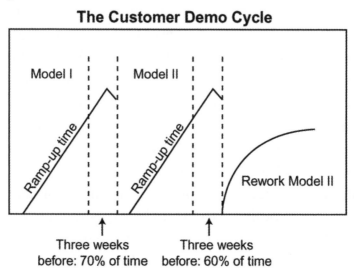

The Customer Demo Cycle

Model I · · Model II · ·

Ramp-up time

Ramp-up time

Rework Model II

↑ Three weeks before: 70% of time

↑ Three weeks before: 60% of time

including himself. He took control of everything he could to the exclusion of those of his own folks and then they started to avoid him, leaving him out of the loop . . . the picture was becoming clearer, Allan thought to himself. He wanted to share his new thoughts with Vicki.

Systems Thinking Principle: Events happen all the time. And they'll continue to happen! Our challenge is to look past the "event" stage and ask other kinds of questions:

- **How many times has this happened? Is there a pattern?**
- **What may be causing this pattern to occur?**
- **How is this event affecting other areas/departments, too?**

Learning Step #7

When you start to ask "What" may be causing this pattern to occur or "Why," you will begin to uncover the fundamental reason(s) for this problem's occurrence. And once you do that, you are on your way to solving the problem. You are also on your way to becoming a systems thinker!

8

Structure Influences Behavior

Allan leaned into the front door with his right shoulder to push it open. After dropping his luggage and briefcase in the front foyer, he glanced into the living room to see Vicki curled up on the sofa reading the paper. She sensed his coming closer to her and she opened her arms to give him a warm embrace and a great welcome home kiss. Allan sat as close as he could to her and they slipped into their easy banter and conversation about everyday things since he had been gone. After about 20 minutes, Allan jumped up and exclaimed, "Vic, let's go for a walk . . . I have something to share with you . . . it's about this guy I met and how he helped me out."

Vicki and Allan walked down their favorite path, taking them into the nearby State forest which abutted their home. Allan explained everything to

Vicki . . . how this guy posed these questions that teased out of him this story of how things happened at work with the preparations for the customer demo. "You know," Allan slowly pondered, "there was a real shift in emphasis, too, with this whole situation." "What do you mean by that?" Vicki gently inquired. "He wanted me to think about what was causing our problems rather than who."

"So," Allan continued, "I sketched out the problem and I really see that we've done it this way before . . . like there is a pattern forming." "Same hype and frenetic pace . . . same response from everyone. . . . same ol' vicious cycle."

"Well, what are you going to do to break out of this cycle?" Vicki anxiously wanted to know.

"Damned if I know!" Allan retorted, half-jokingly and somewhat seriously. Actually, he did have an idea. He wanted to get his team together and share with them his experience with the guy on the plane and the insights he was beginning to have. He told Vicki about this.

"Good luck," she answered somewhat sarcastically.

"And what is that supposed to mean?" Allan retorted back.

"Allan, just because you had this awakening, do you really think your team is going to jump up and down with excitement and embrace you wholeheartedly upon your revelation?" She could really cut to the chase when she wanted to, Allan almost smiled from the irony. He now had a great example of what that phrase feels like.

"Well, why wouldn't they, Vic?" Allan inquired.

"Allan, it's the same reason why I wouldn't react that way with my boss after the way he treated me when he finished up my report." "Let me explain, my dear."

She's on a roll, I can tell, Allan mused to himself as he glanced sideways at his wife.

"You have these bright, capable people who basically want to do the best job they can. Sure, sometimes they need guidance or direction as to how to proceed with something, but basically they know what needs to be done. So, they go along doing the best they can. Then—shabam—in comes their illustrious boss who always has the right way of doing things—it's like they have the one and only right answer. So, the dear boss takes over. And the people are left with not finishing their responsibilities. On another level what is happening is that they are also left feeling wounded, that their efforts are not valued, and then they become uninvolved and unmotivated to want to venture forth again because the same cycle usually occurs. Sometimes it can get to the level of eating away at the trust between the boss and his people, too. And then to top it all off, the boss is usually the one who gets rewarded for acting this way. Go figure. . . . "

This was a lot to think about, Allan reflected. Allan and Vicki were quiet for a few minutes as they looped around toward their home again.

After a while, Allan had a question. "But what is the alternative?" "If I don't do anything, the same old pattern will be there and what good will that do anyone?"

Everything that Vicki said made sense. But there was one kernel of wisdom that really clicked with Allan. It's the boss who gets rewarded for this kind of behavior. Allan focused on this thought for a few moments. He was confused. If his way of acting with his team was so "bad," then why did Stu want him to go to Michigan to do the same thing over there? I mean, that is like giving me a great recognition for putting out those fires, for being the hero of the moment. This perplexed Allan; it seemed so contradictory somehow.

Allan poured himself a cup of coffee and retreated to his favorite chair in the study. He absently stared out the window. He had another thought. If this is really the dynamic going on, he really couldn't blame himself for how he reacted. And, he didn't mean to say that to just pat himself on the back or shirk any responsibility, either. He was just beginning to see that if he was being rewarded, in some particular fashion for getting certain results, regardless of the method, then he had to start looking at this cycle from that level if he was going to make any real changes happen. In his mind, he began to see this sequence and he traced it out on the nearby pad of paper. (see figure 4)

First, we have these "events" that happen and we react to them. Then we step back to see how many times something has happened-if there is a pattern. Now, what we are asking is "what's driving or causing these patterns to occur?" There must be some underlying structure to all of this.

Allan began doodling next to his new picture. To him, he was defining "structure" as the hierarchy that was in place, the culture, the reward system . . . all those systems, both tangible and intangible, that can influence a person's behavior.

Allan had the realization that to begin to make any changes, he needed to do two things: 1) begin to work with his team to help them to see how things happened as they did and 2) work on understanding this "structure" thing more.

Allan had his work cut out for him, but as he said to Vicki, "What's the alternative?"

Figure 4 : Results Sequence

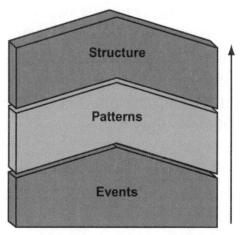

Systems Thinking Principle: A lot of organizations do reward the "hero," the one who comes to the rescue and solves the problem. This reinforces the "putting out the fires," mentality. But what about the others in the organization?

Description of Systems Thinking Diagram

As the manager's interference increases, the 'manager as hero' increases. (The "s" means that what follows the variable will go in the *same* direction; hence, it too will increase.)

As the manager is rewarded as the hero, the level of morale and motivation (of the team members) decreases (an "o" means it goes in the opposite direction). As the level of morale and motivation decreases, individual and team responsibilities for projects also decrease. (Remember, an "s" means it goes in the same direction as the variable that precedes it.)

As the individual and team responsibility decrease, the manager interference increases.

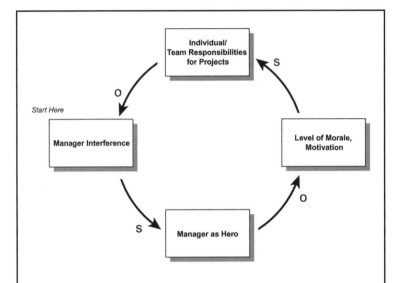

Start Here

Intervention:

The leverage is in (1) not having the manager interfere to the point where the focus is now shifted to the manager and away from the team responsibilities and (2) making sure the system does not reward this "hero" behavior.

To test it out . . .

Try reading the model again. This time with the manager's interference being low.

So, for example:

As the manager's interference decreases, the 'manager as hero' decreases. As the manager is no longer rewarded as the hero, the level of morale and motivation (of the team members) increases. As the level of morale and motivation increases, individual and team responsibilities for projects also increase.

Learning Step #8

Leaders set the example in an organization for prioritizing and being accountable for one's own projects and how they interact with others. We will all still have those "fires," but our objective is to have them be the exception.

9

Getting the Team Back on Track:
Key Breakthrough

Allan was at work by 6:30 a.m. on Monday. He put on a fresh pot of coffee and fired up his PC. Sitting in his chair and gazing out the window, which always seemed like his natural place for coming up with ideas, he started to devise a plan for what he wanted to talk with his team about. He ended up working on this plan for about 2 and ½ hours. He decided to send everyone an e-mail setting up a meeting in their conference room for tomorrow at 9 a.m. to begin talking together.

Allan did a first. He arranged to have bagels, donuts, and coffee on the table for everyone when they came in. Stanley, Bill, Melissa, John, Cecilia, and Susan all slowly filtered into the room. Susan had a casual hi, not her usual cheery self, Allan observed. He tried to shrug that off and concentrate on his agenda.

Allan began by welcoming everyone and stating the purpose of the meeting.

"And, what I'd like to do is share with you what I see has been a problem, why it is a problem, and what we can do about it." Allan presented his "Customer Demo Cycle" chart and his "Events-Patterns-Structure" chart. He was so excited about his new revelations and so glad to be sharing this with his staff. Allan glanced around the room a little. It concerned him that no one was talking.

"So, what I'd like to see us do is to work together even more as a team on our most current problem—the rework of Model II. After all, it was due to the success of the customer demo that all those orders came in and now there is a huge backlog. We need to all help out here."

"Well . . . ?" Allan let his final thought/question kind of trail off, hoping someone would show enough energy to pick up the speaking.

No one did.

"Okay, I take it that everything is okay and we can hit the ground running on this?"

Silent nods and staring down at the table were the only hopes of a reply.

After everyone filed out of the room, Allan slumped in the chair at the front of the conference room and wondered why everyone was not as excited as he was on how he discovered not only the problem but came up with the solution, too!

Meanwhile, the cohort of people that just left the conference room all began to congregate behind the closed door of Susan's office.

"WHAT WAS ALL THAT ABOUT??" John bellowed. "I felt like I was being lectured to." Needless to say, it all went downhill from there, with everyone chiming in. Except Bill who offered, "Yes, but he did bring the bagels . . ." Everyone just shot him a glance that would have melted ice in a polar cave. "Well, he never did that before," Bill countered as he slunk out the door back to his cube.

Allan was truly clueless. It was even more remote than it had been before. Now he wasn't even getting e-mails from his staff! Several days went by. Susan left a voicemail saying that she and John and the rest of the group wanted to meet with Allan on Friday. Same conference room. Same time. This time, they all sat around the conference table. Nobody was sitting at the head of the table. There were no flip charts, overheads, or handouts. Everyone just sat there. Susan took a silent, deep breath and looked over at Allan.

"Allan," she began, "we all met after our meeting on Tuesday and, quite frankly, we were quite upset. We felt like you just came in and talked to us with everything so neatly tied up in one big package-here's the problem, here's why it occurred, here's what we can do about it." We had no say in anything. We weren't even asked if we had any questions. Have you ever noticed that we hardly ever ask questions?" "Why is that?" That is one question (Ha! Notice the irony, Susan quickly surmised as she was talking) that we all asked ourselves, 'How come we don't ask more questions?'

This caught Allan off guard. He never thought of that. Good question, he amusedly pondered. "I was just so excited about what I discovered," Allan offered.

"We all could see that, Allan, and we don't want to take that excitement away," Sue offered.

"Well, what could I have done differently?" Allan genuinely inquired.

"Sometimes it is how we say or do something that makes all the difference, Allan," Sue added.

There seemed to be a breakthrough here.

Allan, John, Susan, Melissa, Bill, Stanley and Cecilia all sat around for the next three hours, totally engrossed in their emerging conversation. Questions were starting to be asked, some people were getting defensive, sometimes there was even silence. But, something was beginning to happen. There was a cohesiveness that was beginning to happen with this group. There was also a new enthusiasm for how Allan captured and synthesized the customer demo problem. His team liked seeing the "big picture" of this issue. They all agreed to begin to work together as a team to tackle the rework problems, but even more importantly, to begin to strategize about how to even out the whole customer demo cycle. This was going to take some time but at least they were all enthusiastic about doing something differently that would benefit them in the long run.

They all set a new date and time to begin strategizing a more effective customer demo schedule to reduce the ramp-up time and address the rework issue. Susan began to wonder, though, wouldn't that involve working with engineering and folks from manufacturing? She quickly put that thought out of her head. She just wanted to concentrate on her product development team for now.

Allan headed back to his office. He was quite pleased. He sat down in his favorite chair and thought about what had just taken place. A new beginning, he thought. A different way of looking at things that holds such great potential to bring people together to look at problems from such a bigger perspective. A quiet peacefulness filled Allan's demeanor. He thought about the man on the plane. The man on the plane had this aura about him . . . that he didn't let too many things ruffle him. Allan wondered if it was because of how he viewed the world; he was able to assimilate the daily events into a more cohesive picture where he could then anticipate the dynamics of a situation. Allan carried this thought forward. What if by thinking this way one is able to be less stressed out? And, if there is less stress, heck, you'd probably feel-and look-better, or even younger, Allan contemplated. That's probably why the man on the plane looked so good for his age! Allan was getting carried away with his thinking. But, he also couldn't help checking out his reflection in the mirror just to see if his new-found inner peacefulness was paying off. Give it time, give it time . . . Allan thought to himself.

Systems Thinking Principle: Behavior will sometimes get worse before it gets better. Expect this to happen.

Learning Step #9

When you are making changes in your organization, expect that behavior may actually worsen. This is where resistance is rearing its head. As the leader, continue on your course of action while still recognizing others' fears, questions, anxieties. It will turn around and go in the anticipated direction.

10

*Working Cross-Functionally:
The Next Big Challenge*

Allan felt good. His team was really starting to work on issues together, very cohesively and very smoothly. He has noticed, however and much to his dismay, that when it comes to that rework problem, he has sensed reluctance, especially from Susan, that nobody wants to work with engineering or manufacturing beyond asking cursory questions or requests for information. Allan realized he needs to address this at some point. Although, he remembers all too clearly the last time Allan brought this subject up. Susan was the first to offer a protest. "Why do we have to work with them? They have their own ideas, ways of working, and if we start sharing our ideas with them, they will probably get all the credit and recognition." Allan had seen this "us" versus "them" mentality before. Having just come back from an off-site with the senior management team, Allan knows that this kind of separateness among organizational entities is going to become a thing of the past. Actually, the more he thought about this divisional dichotomy, the more perplexed he became. How does one even approach something like this? He decided to do something rather differently today. He was going to spend some quiet, reflective time in his office today, with the door closed, just to think.

It's the first day of Spring, Allan thought, as he looked out his office window. There was a slight wind but the sun was shining brightly over the buildings. Allan really enjoyed the work he did. He loved working with people although, as he sat there pondering, he couldn't help but think how things really just went along in an organization. Yes, problems were solved and new problems popped up for attention. People were working really hard. Long hours are now the norm. Why did it always hum along in the same way, though? There weren't any real breakthroughs in how people interacted. He started to think about his wife Vicki's issue with her manager. She is still at arm's length with him, no significant changes there. It is like a superficial veneer. Even with his own team, they are great people and they really get into their projects but it is like its own cocoon. When Allan thought about Susan's comment, 'Why do we have to work with them,' he asked himself, why does it have to be that way? What can help an organization break through its current way of being to embrace new levels of growth?

Allan stopped dead in his tracks. He just had one of those flashes of insight. It was so simple and profound at the same time. When he really thought about it, he realized, everyone is so wrapped up in finding the answers to something. They find the answers to today's challenges and then move on. What about asking new questions? Those kind of questions that tease one's mind? That considers bigger things? So rather than just jumping to conclusions, like we all do, or quickly solving today's issues, why can't we ask, "Well, what would that look like if . . ." or "What would happen if we started working with other departments?" And those kinds of questions could then lead to other questions. . . . deeper questions. As Allan pictured this, what emerged is the thought that as one asks deeper questions of others and of the organization, it is really asking each one of us to look more deeply into ourselves. To test assumptions and patterns of thoughts that we probably don't even know how they got formed. How exciting, Allan thought. How outright fearful it could be, too. People will need to feel like they can take that risk. How does one create that kind of environment? Allan pondered.

Allan felt like he was on to something. Something that holds the promise of greater growth for individuals, teams and the whole organization. All he has to do is articulate the questions so people can start to dig deeper into their own thinking. Now, where's the best place to begin? Allan bemusedly asked himself.

Learning Step #10

Leaders have a great opportunity to help their organizations grow to greater levels of success. Encourage your team—and yourself—to ask different kinds of questions . . . questions that nudge the status quo, that get underneath the surface, that encourage all to explore unforeseen possibilities. The results could pave the way for influencing new pathways of growth for all.

RECOMMENDED RESOURCES FOR LEADERSHIP AND ORGANIZATION DEVELOPMENT

Best Practice Guidebooks

Linkage's Best Practice Guidebooks for Teams, Process Improvement, and Tools

These self-directed, self-paced, practical guidebooks provide best practice tools, processes, and models needed to be an effective manager or change leader, improve processes, and enable teams. All processes, models, and tools have been integrated and implemented with positive measurable change at such organizations as **Raytheon, Morton, Beatrice Foods, Ellerbe Beckett, GE Capital, Barclays Bank, and Volvo.** The guidebooks have been effectively used by vice presidents, managers, supervisors, work team leaders, project managers, and other industry leaders across all major vertical industries.

The Tools Guidebook describes the tools of process improvement as well as how and when to apply them. Each tool provides an in-depth description of the tool including how to use it, when to use it, what it will achieve, why it should be used, a step-by-step approach to implementation, and coaching tips on how to properly enforce the tool's effectiveness. . . . . MTG / $99.00

The Teams Guidebook describes how to form, charter, operate, enhance, and disband various types of teams - in addition to teaching team governance, team behavior, and how to create a high performance team . . . . TG / $99.00

The Process Improvement Guidebook brings the reader through a step-by-step guide to process improvement. Each of the 10 chapters provides instructions and details as to how to carry out the steps. At the end of each chapter there is a section of "do's" and "don'ts" followed by a checklist to ensure that you have completed the step . . . . PG / $99.00

Special Offer! Purchase all 3 valuable guidebooks for just $225.00!

Best Practice Handbooks

Linkage, Inc.'s Best Practices in Knowledge Management and Organizational Learning Handbook

Foreword by Hubert Saint-Onge
Louis Carter, Phil Harkins and Amy Timmins, Editors

Through in-depth "how-to" case studies, over 100 "take-away"exhibits, and research from the world's foremost organizations, this best practice handbook provides practical,easy-to-apply training, models, tools, research and other essential elements fordesigning, delivering, evaluating and learning successful KM/OL programs. Included in the handbook are: Microsoft, AT&T, Hewlett-Packard, Shell Oil Company, Ernst & Young, the World Bank, Buckman Labs, Norske Skog Flooring and more! The "how-to" case studies define KM/OL lexicon, evaluate return on investment, explain how to create a business case for KM/OL, and detail all stages of the KM/OL process.

"How-To" Case Studies: Learn how world-class organizations made effective use of knowledge and reinforced learning to create a lasting change in corporate culture and organizational performance including Buckman Labs' 20-year KM/OL program, Microsoft's taxonomy management system, and Hewlett Packard's integrated KM/OL system.

Models: Benchmark against specific KM/OL models, including: Microsoft's Knowledge Management Architecture; AT&T's Information Knowledge Enterprise; Hewlett Packard's learning community; and the World Bank's Pillars of Knowledge Sharing.

Tools: Learn how to implement cutting-edge KM/OL tools, including: Massachusetts General Hospital's causal-loop diagrams; Microsoft's stakeholder survey; Ernst & Young's balanced scorecard for performance evaluation; and the World Bank's thematic self-assessment and KM action tool.

Training: Choose among best practice training interventions, including Norske Skog Flooring's experiential learning; InFocus' Fusion Workshops; Ernst & Young's Center for Business Knowledge; Shell Oil's communities of practice.

Research: Apply trends and findings from this book to build a business case within your organization. Learn about: top critical success factors for designing and delivering KM/OL initiatives; most popular evaluation methods; technologies needed; budgets required; and more!

BPKM/OL **$89.95**

Linkage Inc.'s Best Practices in Organization and Human Resources Development Handbook

Foreword by Richard Beckhard
Louis Carter, David Giber and Marshall Goldsmith, Editors

Linkage selected 17 best practice organization and HR development initiatives in all major industries, for organizations such as Johnson & Johnson, Kraft Foods, Media One Group, Xerox, Boeing, Sun Microsystems, Nortel Networks, SmithKline Beecham, ServiceMaster, Allstate Insurance, Cellular One and Westinghouse. The book covers 5 of the hottest management topics today: **organization development and change, leadership development, recruitment and retention, performance management, and coaching and mentoring.** Using a case study approach, top practitioners detail the models, tools, training, processes and other critical elements that have made these initiatives so successful. The book also features contributions from such organization and human resources development experts as **Richard Beckhard, Warner Burke, Jay Conger, John Sullivan, Bev Kaye, and Ed Lawler.** It is a rich resource for any manager, OD/HRD practitioner, student, or facilitator of change. Use this handbook to apply learnings from any Linkage workshop.

Case Studies: Learn how 17 world-class organizations achieved their change objectives including how Westinghouse created a safety culture that has become the worldwide standard for safety practices and how Dow Corning implemented an award winning coaching and mentoring system.

Models: Benchmark against Sun Microsystem's 22 behavioral competencies, SmithKline Beecham's use of the Burke-Litwin Model of Organizational Performance and Change, Case Corporation's 15 leadership competencies, Dow Corning's Three-Circle Profile, MediaOne's 360° feedback tool, Boeing's 19 executive competencies and more!

Tools: Learn how to implement cutting edge tools including Kraft Food's organizational assessment tool, Xerox's CSS Empowerment Survey, Cellular One's employee satisfaction survey, and Nortel's change capability evaluation.

Training: Choose among 17 "best-in-class" training and organization interventions including Boeing's action learning program, Johnson & Johnson's Executive Conference, Xerox's work group empowerment initiative, Dow Corning's career fitness and coaching workshops, Kraft Food's high performance work systems training, and ServiceMaster's service culture transformation initiative.

Research: Apply trends and findings from this book to build a business case for change within your organization. Learn about the top critical success factors for designing and delivering an OD/HRD initiative, the most popular evaluation methods, the budgets required, and more!

BPOD/HRD $89.95

The Linkage Toolkit for Developing Leaders

Foreword by Jay Conger
By Linkage Senior and Principal Consultants and Outside Thought Leaders

This toolkit is designed to provide managers and leaders at all levels of your organization with the right tools to become successful and effective. It provides practical advice, ideas, behaviors, assessments, skill-building activities, and methods for leading yourself and others in your daily work.

When it comes to this challenge of leadership and learning, *The Linkage Toolkit for Developing Leaders* is a wonderful resource. You can think of this book like a personal coach - a coach on call. A place for reflection as well as a jumping board for dialogues with your colleagues. This particular coach represents what Linkage has been learning about leadership for quite some time. And it is a multi-faceted coach. It not only provides tools but assessments. It not only helps you think about yourself but your impact on others. It is also a very pragmatic coach who wants you out on the playing field applying what you have learned. Best of all, it is a remarkably comprehensive coach - Linkage's toolkit is packed with all sorts of helpful instruments, cases, diagnostics, and advice. In many ways, this volume is like a filled-to-the-gills tool box. What I particularly like about this book is that we often need help quickly. The tools and assessments in the book are organized in short, 'how-to' sections with examples to illustrate how each is done. It is an easy to use and easy to locate reference source. With internet years running at about 30 days, such quick easy access to information is so important. In addition, there are compartments arranged by the level of leadership challenge you are facing. There are tools for leading yourself, tools for leading individuals, tools for leading teams, and tools for leading your organization. So you'll find a full complement of tools to get the job done.

- Jay Conger, author, Building Leaders

If you are using *The Linkage Toolkit for Developing Leaders* as a quick-reference "toolbox," each of the four major sections is clearly labeled with tabs for easy access. These sections are

Leading Yourself-
The first section is a baseline series of topics and tools that can help you assess and develop your general leadership abilities. Our belief is that you cannot successfully lead others until you can develop the self-awareness and maturity necessary to "lead yourself."

Leading Individuals-
The next section focuses on your role as coach, mentor, and performance manager. Whether in a formal position of authority or not, your ability to hold powerful conversations with staff and colleagues-one-on-one-to set

expectations and influence behavior is critical. This is "ground zero" for effective leadership

Leading Teams-
The engine of change and performance in the modern business enterprise is a leader's use of teams. Your roles as team sponsor, team leader, and team facilitator are central to leveraging members' diversity to successful and innovative outcomes.

Leading Organizations-
The final section addresses the challenges some leaders face as enterprise-wide developers. The roles of organizational architect, process manager, and communicator and implementer of strategy are often the ones we are least schooled in, especially those of you with more technical (and less business) backgrounds.

HOW YOU CAN USE THIS TOOLKIT
Direct Application
Because this toolkit contains actual tools, assessments, exercises, and models you can immediately apply it to your job as a leader in your organization. The assessments, models, references, exercises can be easily implemented and customized to fit your specific personal or organizational leadership needs.

Leadership Development or Organization Development Programs
This book is ideal for your organization's Leadership or Organization Development program. You may apply many of these tools as your organization grows and changes - or when there is a demand to introduce the need for leadership development. Contact one of the Linkage consultants on the biography pages at the end of this book to get a better idea of how Linkage can further assist you in meeting your organization's unique approach to developing leaders and growing in this dynamic business world.

Career or Personal Development
If you are looking for a new job, or simply wanting to improve your leadership abilities, the tools within this book are ideal to practice or apply to your current job.

Linkage Toolkit for Developing Leaders . . . . Price: $159.95

Also inquire about licensing options for each tool within your organization . . .

To Order any of these Titles, contact
Linkage Customer Service at:
781.862.3157
or visit Linkage's website at:
http://www.linkageinc.com